"WHAT HAS BEEN WILL BE AGAIN,
WHAT HAS BEEN DONE WILL BE DONE AGAIN;
THERE IS NOTHING NEW UNDER THE SUN."
—KING SOLOMON

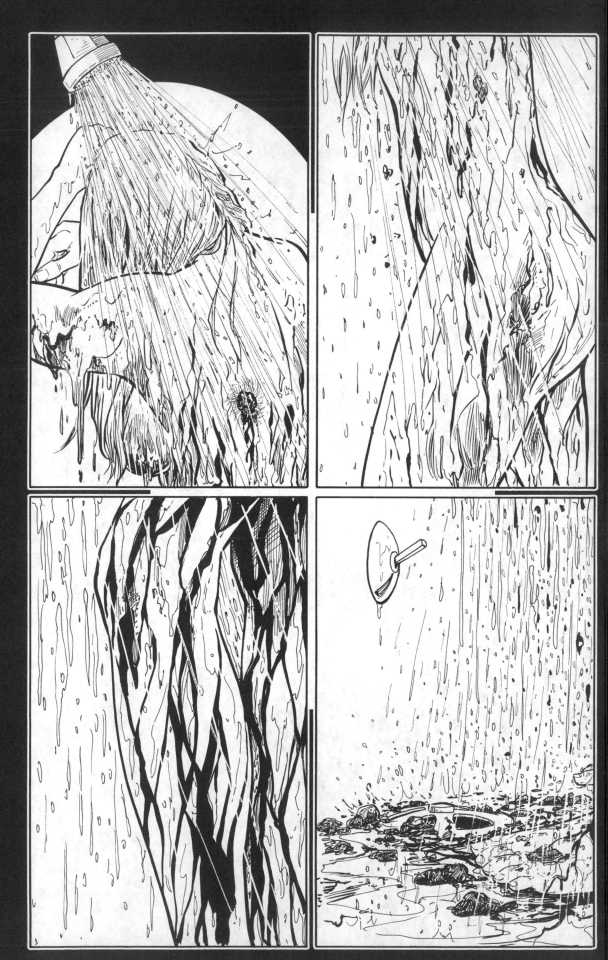

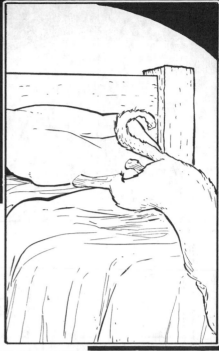

That's getting really old, Euclid. You don't have to run and hide every time I walk into the room. I'm not going to eat you.

I just look like I will, right?

I'm afraid you're going to have to get used to it, little buddy. This is how I am now, I guess. Rachel Beck... the girl who won't die.

Bury me—

And I'll dig my way out, come home and scare my cat under the bed. Ooh... I'm a monster.

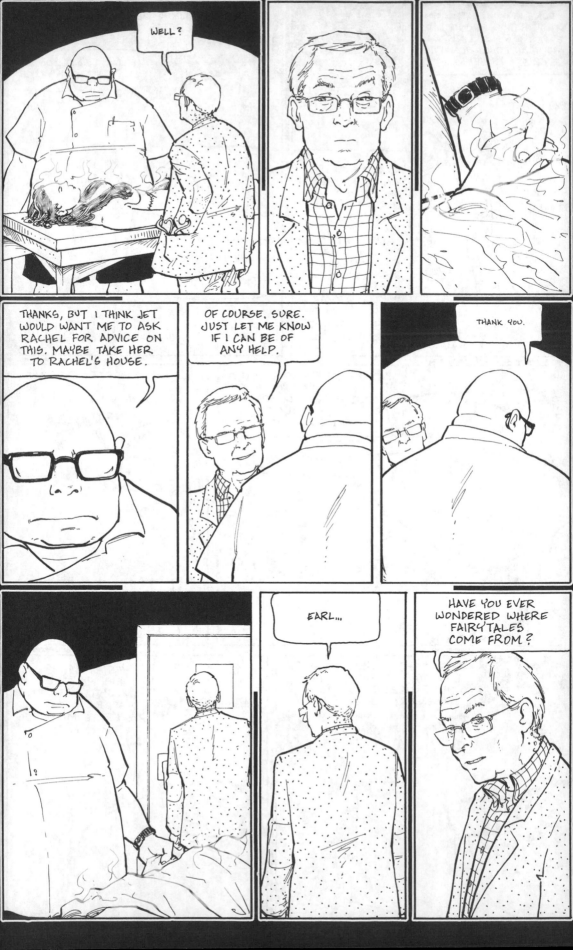

AND WHAT WOKE HER UP?

A KISS.

A KISS FROM THE MAN WHO LOVED HER.

MM HMM, YEAH, THAT'S WHAT THEY TOLD THE CHILDREN. BUT THE STORY CHARLES PERRAULT WROTE IN 1690 WAS ACTUALLY INSPIRED BY A WELL KNOWN EVENT THAT OCCURRED 100 YEARS BEFORE HIM, IN THE COURT OF PRINCESS ZELLANDINE.

EVER HEARD OF HER?

NO.

SHE TOO WAS UNWAKEABLE. NOT DEAD, BUT NOT ALIVE. TODAY WE MIGHT SAY SHE WAS IN A COMA BUT, BACK THEN, ALL THEY KNEW WAS ZELLANDINE HAD FALLEN INTO "A DEEP SLEEP", AND NO ONE COULD WAKE HER.

WHAT DID THEY DO WITH HER?

WELL, SHE WASN'T DECOMPOSING, SO THEY LAID HER TO REST IN A TOWER AND PRAYED FOR HER.

THERE WAS A MAN, OF COURSE. HIS NAME WAS TROYLUS, AND HE LOVED THE PRINCESS VERY MUCH. TROYLUS WAS AWAY WHEN THIS HAPPENED, WORKING TO EARN ZELLANDINE'S HAND IN MARRIAGE, WHICH HE DID.

BUT, WHEN AT LAST HE RETURNED, HE FOUND HER IN THE TOWER.

HEARTBROKEN, TROYLUS SAT BY HIS FIANCEE'S SIDE FOR WEEKS UNTIL, ONE DAY,... OVERCOME WITH GRIEF...

HE KISSED HER?

HE RAPED HER.

THAT'S DISGUSTING.

THAT'S THE TRUTH.

≥ SIGH ≥

WHAT HAPPENED ... AFTER THAT?

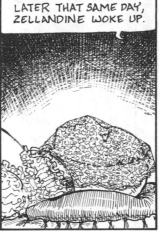
LATER THAT SAME DAY, ZELLANDINE WOKE UP.

IMMEDIATELY SHE KNEW SOMETHING WAS WRONG, OF COURSE. SHE KNEW SHE'D BEEN VIOLATED.

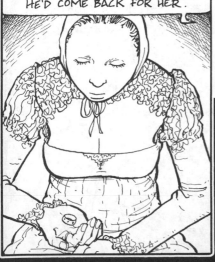
ON HER DRESS, SHE FOUND THE RING SHE'D GIVEN TROYLUS AND SHE KNEW — IT HAD BEEN HIM. TRUE TO HIS WORD, HE'D COME BACK FOR HER.

ZELLANDINE DIDN'T HAVE FAR TO GO TO FIND TROYLUS BECAUSE, WHEN SHE ROSE AND LOOKED OUT THE WINDOW, THERE HE WAS...

ON THE ROCKS BELOW. HIS BODY HAD BURST OPEN LIKE A BAG ON IMPACT, AND ZELLANDINE WAS HELPLESS AS SHE WATCHED A MURDER OF CROWS EAT HER FIANCE'S HEART...

THEN FLY AWAY.

HOW ARE WE LOOKING OUT THERE.?

CLEAR.

HEY, SEE THIS?

THIS... IS GOING TO RUIN YOUR LIFE.

WATCH.

BADDA BING...

CLICK!

BADDA BOOM.

WHEN THEY FIND THIS ON YOUR COMPUTER, YOU'RE GOING TO BE ALL, "THAT'S NOT MINE! I DON'T KNOW HOW THAT GOT ON THERE!"

AND THEY'LL SAY, "SHUT UP, YOU SICK BASTARD! YOU DEGENERATE MONSTER! YOU FUTHERMUCKIN' PERVERT!"

MARY SCOTT... YOU'RE WASTING VENOM.

GO. BRING THEM TO THEIR KNEES BEFORE THE PORCELAIN GOD.

OKAY... DON'T DRINK THE WATER.

DID YOU PUT THE FILES ON HIS COMPUTER?

I DID. TRUST ME, WHEN THEY FIND THESE PICTURES ON HIS HARD DRIVE, HE'S GOING STRAIGHT TO PRISON!

HE MAY NOT EVEN GET A TRIAL. THEY MAY JUST SHOOT HIM.

HANNAH, ARE WE CLEAR TO LEAVE?

SMACK! SMACK! SMACK!

ALL CLEAR.

LADIES, WE'RE DONE HERE. LET'S GO.

DO YOU KNOW WHAT THEY DO TO PERVERTS IN PRISON, FAT ASS?

YOU'RE GOING TO BURRNNN! YOU'RE GOING TO BLEEEED!

SHE HAS ANGER ISSUES.

EH, WHAT ARE YOU GONNA DO — WOLVES ATE HER BROTHER.

MARY SCOTT... LEAVING!

"IF I COULD ONLY REMEMBER MY NAME."
—DAVID CROSBY

1.

2.

3.

4.

5.

6.

7.

8.

9.

SCHIKK!

I'M LOST.

WELL, WE CAN FIX THAT. WHERE DO YOU LIVE?

:SNIFF!:

NO. I MEAN *REALLY* LOST!

LIKE, YOU KNOW...

NO ONE IS TRULY LOST, MY CHILD.

THEY'RE JUST LOOKING IN THE WRONG DIRECTION.

"I WAS RIGHT NOT TO BE AFRAID OF
ANY THIEF BUT MYSELF, WHO WILL
END UP LEAVING ME NOTHING."
—KATHERINE ANNE PORTER

≡ SNORE ≡

SNUKK!

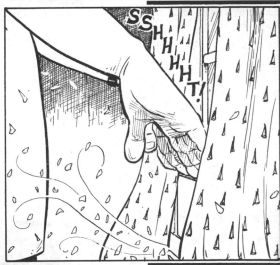

SSHHHHT!

RICK, SOME OF THE CUSTOMERS ARE COMPLAINING OF FEELING SICK.

CRAP! WHAT DID THEY ORDER?

UHMM, I DON'T KNOW... SALADS, CRAB CAKES, RAVIOLI...

PAULO, DID YOU CHECK THE CRAB THIS MORNING?

YEAH, RICK, IT WAS FINE.

RICK, TABLE FOUR FOUND THIS IN THEIR WATER.

WHAT IS IT?

LOOKS LIKE RAT DROPPINGS!

UH, GUYS? GUYS...

OH MY GODDD!

WHOA!

NOT BAD... FOR DEAD. I CAN DO THIS.

NOT SURE WHAT IT'S GOING TO DO TO MY LOVE LIFE, THOUGH... IF I CAN'T FEEL ANYTHING. HUH, I'LL BE JUST LIKE MY MOTHER.

SQUEAK!

SQUEAK!

BRAK!
BRAK!
BRAK!

YEOW!

BLOWP!

≥ SIGH ≤

BRAK! BRAK! BRAK! BLOWP. YEOW!

≥ JEEZ-A-MOMMA! ≤

ARE YOU OKAY?

YOU WENT TO THE BATHROOM?

DO NOT GO IN THERE!

WHAT? NO! THERE'S A RAT!

OH.

WHAT DO YOU MEAN, "OH"? IT'S HUGE AND IT CAME OUT OF THE FAUCET!

KILL IT!

HE HAS AS MUCH RIGHT TO BE ON THE PLANET AS WE DO.

ARE YOU NUTS? IT'S A DISEASED RODENT! KILL IT!

I DON'T WANT TO DESTROY ANYTHING I CAN'T REPLACE. I'LL JUST MOVE IT.

≥ CLICK! ≤

AAAIIEEGH!

SQUEEEEEE!

...AS OFFICIALS SCRAMBLE TO FIND THE SOURCE OF THE CITY'S WATER CONTAMINATION, INVESTIGATORS HAVE ARRESTED CITY WATER MANAGER HECTOR RUIZ AFTER FINDING ILLEGAL PORNOGRAPHY ON HIS OFFICE COMPUTER. MR. RUIZ HAS DENIED ANY KNOWLEDGE OF THE FILES. FOR MORE ON THIS DEVELOPING STORY, WE GO TO...

OUR CHANNEL 8 ACTION REPORTER, BOB BODINE. BOB, WHAT DO YOU HAVE?

DOUG, MANSON'S WATER HAS BECOME HOME TO THOUSANDS OF RATS.

THE QUESTION NOW IS — WHAT CAN WE DO ABOUT IT?

TERRY MOORE
RACHEL RISING
ABSTRACT STUDIO
ISSUE NO.
16
3.99 US

"MANKIND IS A SUMMER FIELD,
BARREN, DRY AND FALLOW."
—LILITH

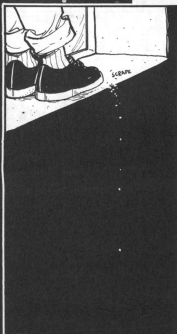

:SIGH:

STILL SNOWING? WILL IT EVER STOP?

OH MY LORD!

CRRAK!

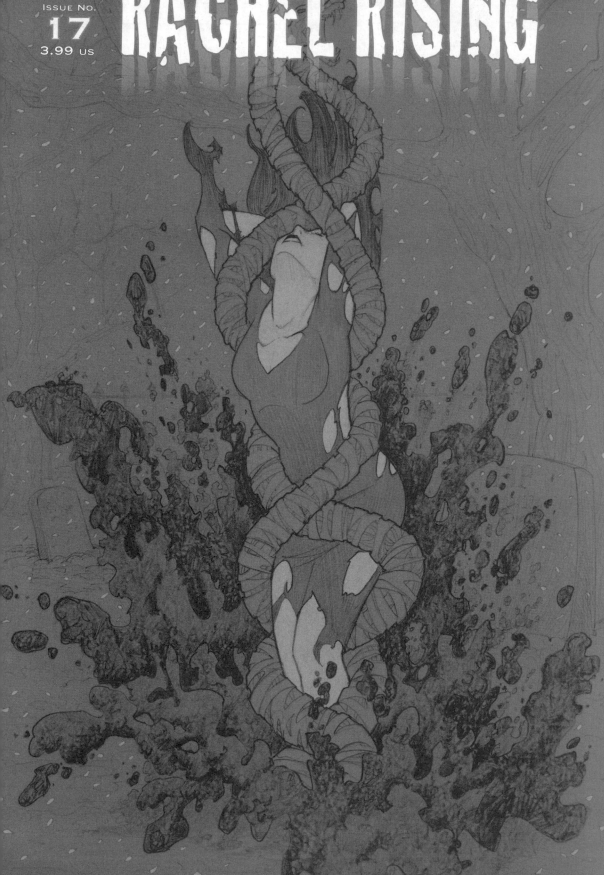

"JUST A SMILE,
JUST A GLANCE.
THE PRINCE OF DARKNESS,
HE JUST WALKED PAST."
—ROY BUCHANAN

WAKING UP IN YOUR OWN GRAVE IS NOT UNHEARD OF. IN FACT, BEFORE MODERN MEDICINE, IT WAS FAIRLY COMMON. PEOPLE WHO APPEARED TO BE LIFELESS AND UNRESPONSIVE TO PIN PRICKS AND BREATHING MIRRORS WERE SIMPLY DECLARED DEAD.

THERE ARE MANY CASES ON FILE OF NOISES COMING FROM A NEW GRAVE, DIGGING UP THE COFFIN... FINDING GOUGE MARKS INSIDE THE LID...

AND A CORPSE WITH BLOODY FINGERS.

THEY WEREN'T ALIVE?

RARELY. BY THE TIME THEY WERE EXHUMED, MOST PEOPLE HAD DIED OF HEART FAILURE DUE TO TERROR AND SUFFOCATION.

IN EACH CASE, THE VICTIM WAS INTERRED BECAUSE THEY GAVE THE APPEARANCE OF DEATH WHEN IN FACT, THEY WERE BURIED ALIVE.

THAT'S AWFUL.

YES, IT IS. AND, APPARENTLY IT HAPPENED SO OFTEN THAT FAMILIES BURIED LOVED ONES WITH A BELL ON THE GRAVE, ATTACHED TO A STRING IN THE COFFIN—

JUST IN CASE.

THEY ALSO STOPPED BURYING THE DEAD ON THE DAY OF DEATH AND MANDATED A 24-HOUR WAITING PERIOD. SOMEBODY WAS REQUIRED TO STAY UP WITH THE BODY AND MAKE SURE IT DIDN'T WAKE UP.

SO, HOLDING A WAKE...

JUST A TRADITION NOW, OF COURSE.

BUT IT USED TO BE YOUR LAST CHANCE.

AUNT JOHNNY?

...

AUNT JOHNNY.

HMM?

CLICK!

YOU'RE NOT GOING TO FIND THE ANSWERS TO ME IN A MEDICAL DATABASE.

RACHEL, THERE'S A LOGICAL EXPLANATION FOR EVERYTHING GOING ON HERE.

PHYSICS AND MEDICINE ARE LIKE AUTO MECHANICS — JUST ONE PIECE CONNECTED TO ANOTHER.

YOU'RE RIGHT. THAT'S HOW MAGIC WORKS, TOO.

MAGIC? RACHEL...

ALL MY NATURAL CAUSES EXPIRED A LONG TIME AGO, JOHNNY. I KNOW THAT NOW. EVERY DAY I REMEMBER MORE AND MORE ABOUT MY LIFE.

THAT'S ONLY NATURAL. AS YOUR BODY REPAIRS ITSELF...

BUT THAT'S THE POINT... IT'S NOT REPAIRING! LOOK, I'VE HAD THIS SINCE THE ACCIDENT.

OH MY GOD.

AND, I HATE TO ADMIT IT AFTER WHAT YOU JUST SAID BUT, I DON'T FEEL IT. I MEAN, IT'S THERE AND I SEE IT, BUT I DON'T FEEL IT.

HOLY CRAP. RACHEL...

I CAN SEE RIGHT THROUGH YOU.

SNAP!

AM I SUPPOSED TO HAVE ONE OF THOSE? 'CAUSE I DON'T THINK I DO... HAVE ONE. AM I MISSING OUT?

STUFF IT.

REALLY? RIGHT HERE?

RACHEL, COME HERE. LET ME LOOK AT THAT CLOSER.

NO, AUNT JOHNNY...

YOU'RE NOT GOING TO LEARN ANYTHING BY EXAMINING MY HOLE OR JET'S NECK. IF ANYTHING, THEY PROVE MY POINT...

HEH HEH.

DID I SAY SOMETHING FUNNY?

YOU SAID...

SHUT UP.

AUNT JOHNNY, WE'RE NOT STANDING HERE FOR MEDICAL REASONS. THIS IS WITCHCRAFT.

I KNOW YOU DO. BUT, THAT'S THE ANSWER. THE SOONER YOU ACCEPT IT, THE SOONER WE CAN FIX THINGS.

I SERIOUSLY DOUBT THAT.

LIKE, YOUR HOLE.

LIKE MY HOLE.

"SOMEBODY CALLING
CALLING MY NAME;
SOMEBODY WALKING
OVER MY GRAVE."
—ROBIN TROWER

SSSSSSSSS

HECTOR RUIZ?

YES.

HAVE A SEAT.

ARE YOU A LAWYER?

NO. I'M DETECTIVE CORPELL, WITH THE POLICE. I'VE BEEN LOOKING INTO YOUR CASE. YOU DON'T ADD UP, MR. RUIZ.

I AM INNOCENT.

HMM.

ARMY VET, HONORABLE DISCHARGE, STARTED WORKING WITH THE CITY IN '99, NIGHT CLASSES AT COMMUNITY COLLEGE, FAMILY MAN, VOLUNTEER FIREMAN, NO PRIOR ARRESTS ...

SUDDENLY YOU'RE FACING A SLEW OF CHARGES RANGING FROM ACTS OF TERRORISM AGAINST THE CITY TO USING A CITY COMPUTER FOR DISTRIBUTION OF CHILD PORNOGRAPHY.

I WOULD NEVER DO THESE THINGS.

MR. RUIZ, I'M INCLINED TO BELIEVE YOU. I'VE BEEN GOING THROUGH SECURITY RECORDINGS OF YOUR OFFICE.

CAN YOU TELL ME WHO THIS IS?

THAT'S MY DESK! WHAT IS THIS?

WHO IS SHE?

I DON'T KNOW!

HOW IS THIS POSSIBLE?!

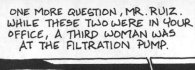

ONE MORE QUESTION, MR. RUIZ. WHILE THESE TWO WERE IN YOUR OFFICE, A THIRD WOMAN WAS AT THE FILTRATION PUMP.

WHAT?!

DO YOU KNOW...

HER?

NO!

WHAT IS SHE DOING? SHE SHOULD NOT BE THERE!

SHE DEPOSITED SOMETHING INTO THE CITY WATER SUPPLY... WHILE HER FRIENDS UPLOADED CHILD PORNOGRAPHY ONTO YOUR COMPUTER. AND YOU SLEPT THROUGH IT ALL OR WERE RENDERED UNCONSCIOUS.

THIS IS *TERRIBLE!* WHY WOULD THEY DO SUCH TERRIBLE THINGS?

I WAS HOPING YOU COULD TELL ME. BUT YOU CLAIM YOU DON'T KNOW ANY OF THESE WOMEN, YOU DON'T KNOW HOW THEY GOT INTO YOUR OFFICE OR WHY THEY COMMITTED THESE ACTS.

NO, SIR.

MR. CORPELL, I'M STILL IN TROUBLE?

MR. RUIZ, I THINK WE'RE ALL IN TROUBLE.

YOU LOOK LIKE A PERSON WITH DOUBTS.

I WONDER SOMETIMES IF ANY OF THIS IS REAL —

OR IS IT JUST A BUSINESS, SELLING HOPE TO PEOPLE WHO CAN'T AFFORD IT?

CLEVER PEOPLE HAVE BEEN ASKING THAT QUESTION SINCE THE IRON AGE, ZOE. THE ANSWER REMAINS THE SAME.

AND...?

BUSINESS IS GOOD.

COME ON, I HAVE SOMETHING TO SHOW YOU.

THANK YOU FOR SLAUGHTERING THE GOAT LAST NIGHT.

WE...

I'M SERIOUS... THANK YOU! YOU DID US A BIG FAVOR. THAT'S WHAT IT WAS THERE FOR. WE GAVE THE MEAT TO OUR HOMELESS SHELTER. WHAT YOU DID HELPED PEOPLE.

I'M VERY PROUD OF YOU.

REALLY!

ZOE, YOU HAVE A REMARKABLE GIFT. THE KIND THAT COMES ALONG ONCE IN A GENERATION. USED WISELY, YOU COULD BE A GREAT ASSET TO THE COMMUNITY.

INSTEAD OF FEELING LIKE AN OUTCAST, YOU SHOULD BE PRAISED FOR YOUR WORK. PEOPLE SHOULD RESPECT YOU.

WOULD YOU LIKE THAT?

YOU THINK KILLING IS A GIFT?

THE WAY YOU DO IT — YES!

WHAT KIND OF PRIEST ARE YOU?

THE KIND WHO IS FED UP WITH PREDATORS PICKING OFF THE INNOCENTS ONE BY ONE. THE PEOPLE NEED A DEFENDER, ZOE. THEY NEED JUSTICE!

I THOUGHT THAT WAS GOD'S JOB.

WELL, GOD'S NOT HERE, IS HE? WE MUST REPRESENT HIM.

WHAT DO YOU THINK HE HAS PLANNED FOR THE BAD PEOPLE OF THIS WORLD?

NOTHING GOOD.

EXACTLY. AND THAT IS THE JOB OF HIS... SPECIAL PEOPLE. YOU ARE ONE OF HIS SPECIAL PEOPLE, ZOE.

I THINK THIS WILL BE EASIER TO UNDERSTAND IF I SHOW YOU.

FOLLOW ME.

I'M GOING TO LAY A NEW WORLD AT YOUR FEET, THEN YOU CAN SEE WHAT YOUR INSTINCTS TELL YOU.

THIS WAS AN EXERCISE ROOM FOR THE CLERGY BACK IN THE FIFTIES.

NOW IT'S A FORGOTTEN STOREROOM AND I HAVE THE ONLY KEY.

IT HAS SOME INTERESTING FEATURES, THOUGH.

LIKE WHAT?

A SHOWER.

MR. BUNDY IS ONE OF THE PREDATORS I WAS TELLING YOU ABOUT, ZOE. WORKS IN A HARDWARE STORE, VERY FRIENDLY, SPENDS HIS NIGHT SCOUTING NEARBY TOWNS FOR RUNAWAY BOYS. THERE ARE TWENTY-TWO OF THEM BURIED IN A MASS GRAVE UNDER HIS BASEMENT.

MMGGH!

THIS IS SICK! WHAT'S HE DOING HERE?!

HE'S HERE FOR YOU, ZOE. MR. BUNDY WILL BE YOUR FIRST RIGHTEOUS ACT.

JUSTICE SERVED FOR TWENTY-TWO DEAD BOYS.

AND MR. BUNDY.

MMGH!

I'M LEAVING. THANKS FOR THE BED.

I'LL MANAGE.

THE DAYS OF CHARITY ARE NUMBERED FOR YOU, ZOE MANN.

YOU'RE GROWING UP.

ARE YOU READY FOR THAT? NEW RULES, KIDDO. NEW RULES.

IN A FEW YEARS, YOU'LL BE STANDING EYE TO EYE WITH THE BUNDY'S OF THE WORLD.

IF YOU DON'T KNOW WHAT YOU'RE DOING YOU MIGHT END UP UNDER A BASEMENT.

WHAT DO YOU WANT PRIEST?

I WANT TO HELP YOU BE ALL YOU CAN BE, ZOE. YOU HAVE A GIFT BUT, LIKE ANY PRODIGY, YOUR TALENT MUST BE DEVELOPED.

ANIMALS LIKE THIS ARE EXTREMELY DANGEROUS. LET ME TEACH YOU THE SAFE WAY TO HANDLE THEM.

HOW DO YOU MEAN?

WELL, TAKE YOUR GREAT GRANDFATHER, FOR EXAMPLE. HE WAS A MASTER.

WHAT? HOW...

ROBERT MANN. I'LL SHOW YOU.

ROBERT WAS THE FASTEST I'VE EVER SEEN. HE ALWAYS CAME UP FROM BEHIND AND, QUICK AS A BLINK, COVERED THE MOUTH, PULLED THE HEAD BACK, AND SLICED THE THROAT FROM EAR TO EAR. ALL ONE MOVE. SEE?

MMPH!

THIS SEVERED THE WIND PIPE AND BOTH CAROTID ARTERIES. SO THE BODY MADE NO SOUND AND DROPPED LIKE A ROCK.

THE FIRST CUT'S MESSY BUT YOU'RE BEHIND THE BODY, SEE? YOU STAY CLEAN.

I KNOW. THAT'S HOW SOLDIERS DO IT.

AH, BUT THE DIFFERENCE HERE IS, YOU MAY WANT TO CONTINUE WORKING WITH THE ANIMAL. NOW YOU CAN WORK FROM ANY POSITION WITHOUT FEAR OF SPRAY BECAUSE THE BLOOD PRESSURE'S GONE.

IN LESS THAN A SECOND, THE ANIMAL IS YOURS.

MMGH!

YOUR GREAT GRANDFATHER ≡HEH≡ I REMEMBER HE MADE A GAME OF IT, TO SEE HOW MUCH HE COULD ACCOMPLISH BEFORE THE BODY EXPIRED. BY THE END HE WAS...

QUITE PHENOMENAL.

SO... WOULD YOU LIKE TO TRY IT?

MMPH!

HOW COULD YOU POSSIBLY KNOW MY GREAT GRANDFATHER? THAT'S IMPOSSIBLE.

I'M OLDER THAN I LOOK. YOU UNDERSTAND, DON'T YOU?

WE'RE ALIKE, YOU AND I.

SPECIAL.

THE KNIFE I GAVE YOU... THAT WAS YOUR GREAT GRANDFATHER'S. YOU HAVE IT WITH YOU?

CALL IT JACK.

I THOUGHT YOU SAID THIS BE-LONGED TO A FRIEND OF YOURS NAMED JACK?

IT DID. AND NOW IT BELONGS TO YOU. SHALL WE?

22 BOYS UNDER HIS BASEMENT.

JUSTICE.

YADA YADA.

MMGH?!

WHAT WAS MY GREAT GRANDFATHER'S RECORD?

MMGH!

MMGH!

MMGH

ZIP!

I'LL TELL YOU WHEN.

RIP!

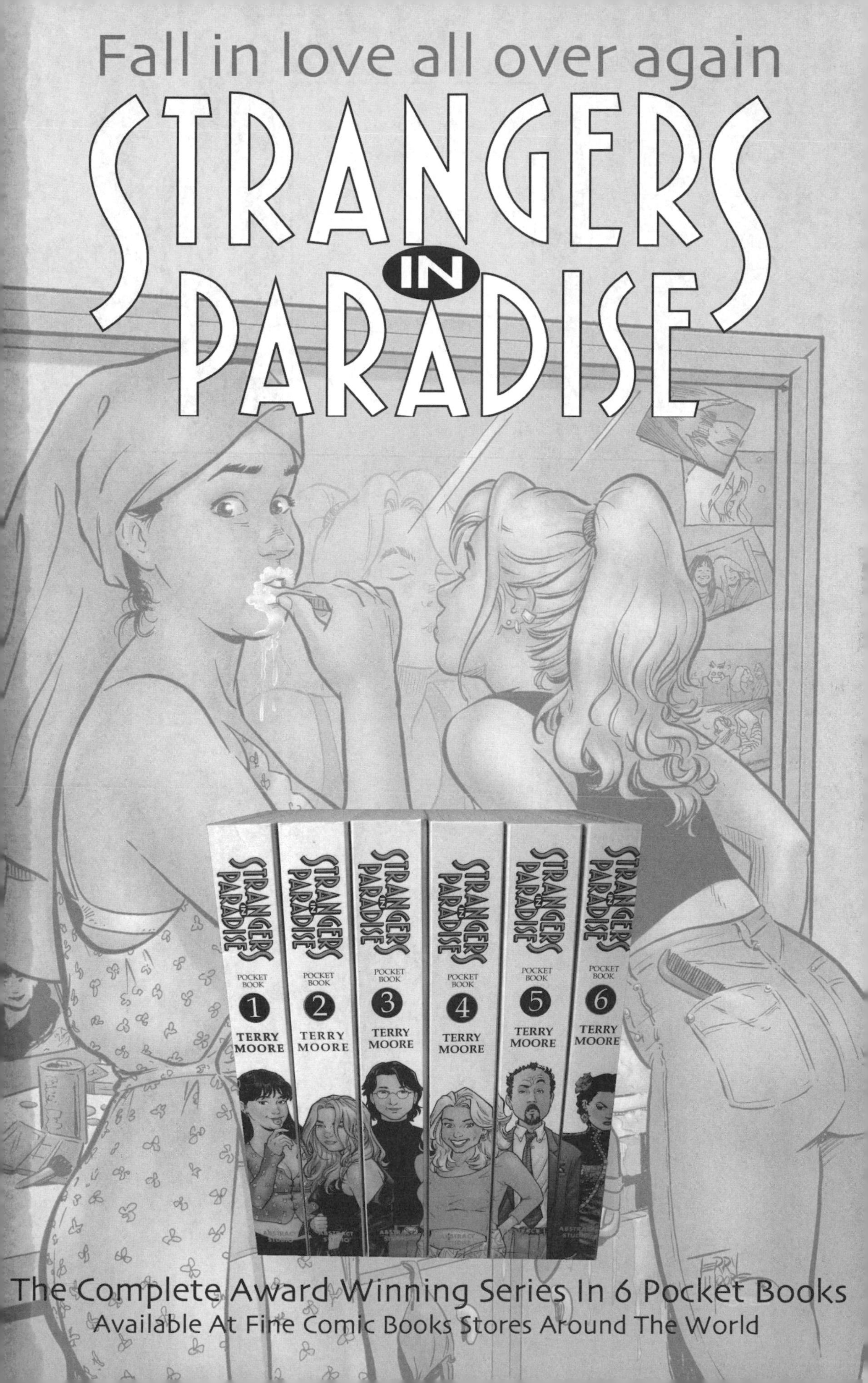

Fall in love all over again
STRANGERS IN PARADISE
STRANGERS IN PARADISE POCKET BOOK 1 TERRY MOORE
STRANGERS IN PARADISE POCKET BOOK 2 TERRY MOORE
STRANGERS IN PARADISE POCKET BOOK 3 TERRY MOORE
STRANGERS IN PARADISE POCKET BOOK 4 TERRY MOORE
STRANGERS IN PARADISE POCKET BOOK 5 TERRY MOORE
STRANGERS IN PARADISE POCKET BOOK 6 TERRY MOORE
The Complete Award Winning Series In 6 Pocket Books
Available At Fine Comic Books Stores Around The World

STORY & ART
TERRY MOORE

TERRYMOOREART.COM

ROBYN MOORE
Publisher

Published by
ABSTRACT STUDIO
P. O. Box 271487, Houston, Texas 77277

email: SIPNET@STRANGERSINPARADISE.COM

Printed in Canada